CHILD'S PLAY
Science

David B. Y. Ta[...]

Illustrated by Maung Han

© 1997 Federal Publications (S) Pte Ltd
© 2000 Times Media Private Limited
© 2003 Marshall Cavendish International (Singapore) Private Limited

Published by Marshall Cavendish Education
An imprint of Marshall Cavendish International (Singapore) Private Limited
A member of Times Publishing Limited
Times Centre, 1 New Industrial Road, Singapore 536196
Customer Service Hotline: (65) 6411 0820
E-mail: fps@sg.marshallcavendish.com
Website: www.marshallcavendish.com/education/sg

First published 1997
Reprinted 1998, 1999, 2000, 2003, 2005
Second impression 2006
Reprinted 2007, 2008

ISBN 978-981-01-0752-9

Printed in Singapore by C.O.S. Printers Pte Ltd

Marshall Cavendish
Education

Contents

My Body

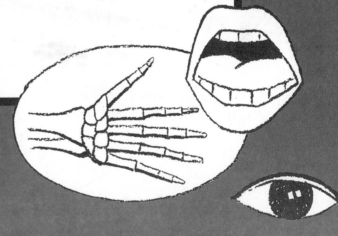

This is Shawn.

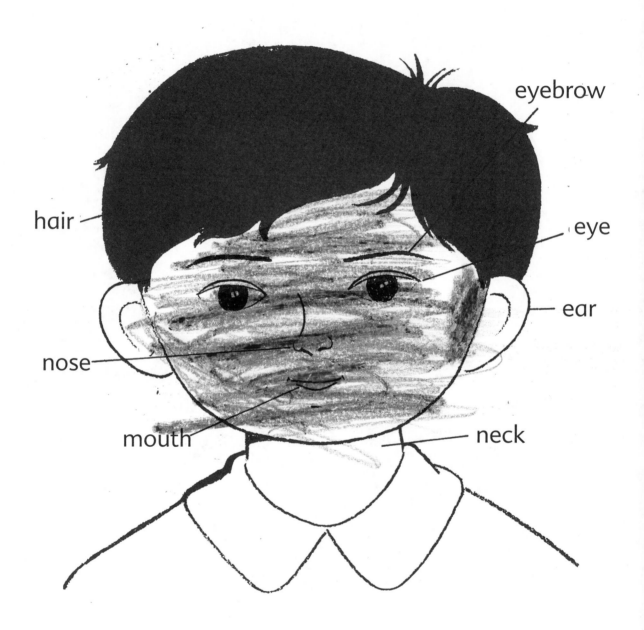

eyebrow

hair

eye

ear

nose

mouth

neck

Colour Shawn's head.

This is Linda.

(A) nose   (B) hair   (C) ear

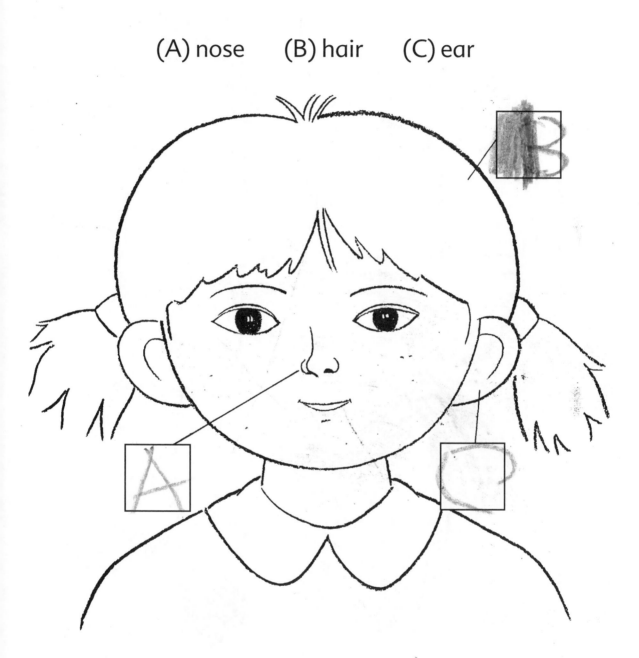

- **Colour Linda.**
- **Write the letters A, B or C in the correct boxes.**

Linda sees with her eyes.
She cannot see without them.

- **What does Linda see?**
- **Colour the objects she is looking at.**

Shawn is listening to music.
He cannot hear without his ears.

- Look at the objects in the picture.
- Colour those that make sounds.

Linda tastes with her **tongue.**

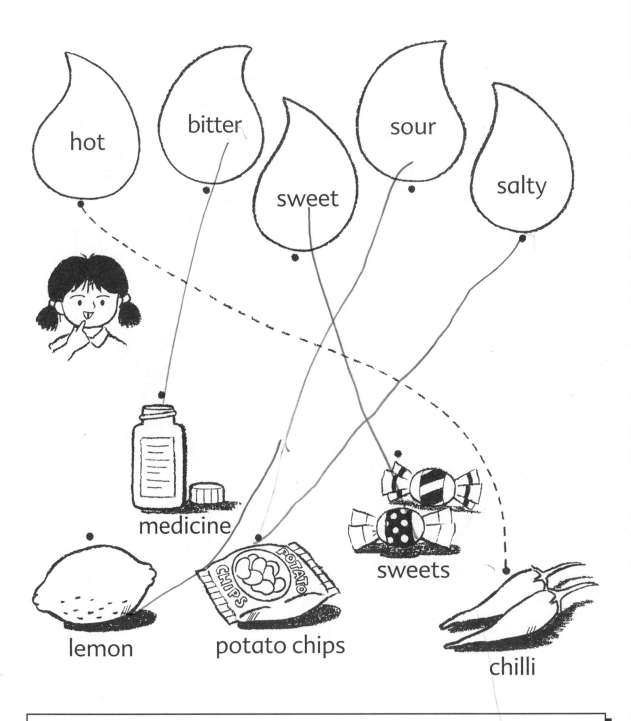

Help Linda join the pictures to the correct words of taste.

There are **muscles** in our body.
Muscles enable parts of our body to do many things.

(A) fingers   (B) hips   (C) head   (D) eyes   (E) mouth

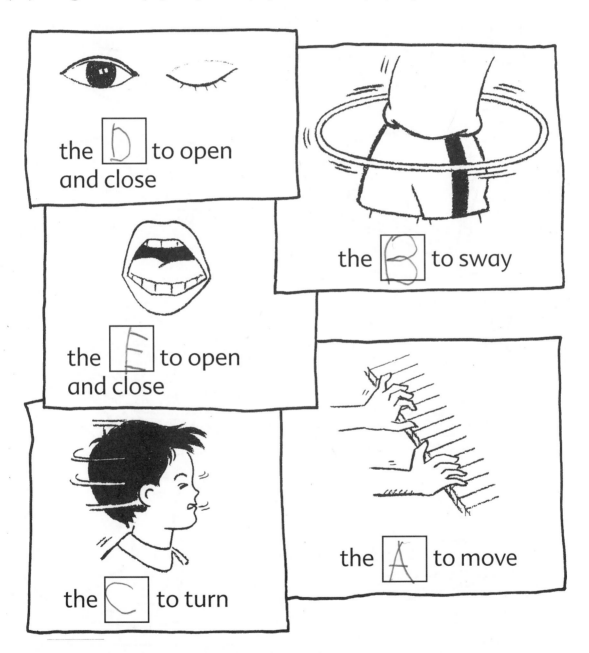

the D to open and close

the B to sway

the E to open and close

the C to turn

the A to move

Write the letters A, B, C, D or E in the correct boxes.

We have **bones**.
Some are big. Others are small.

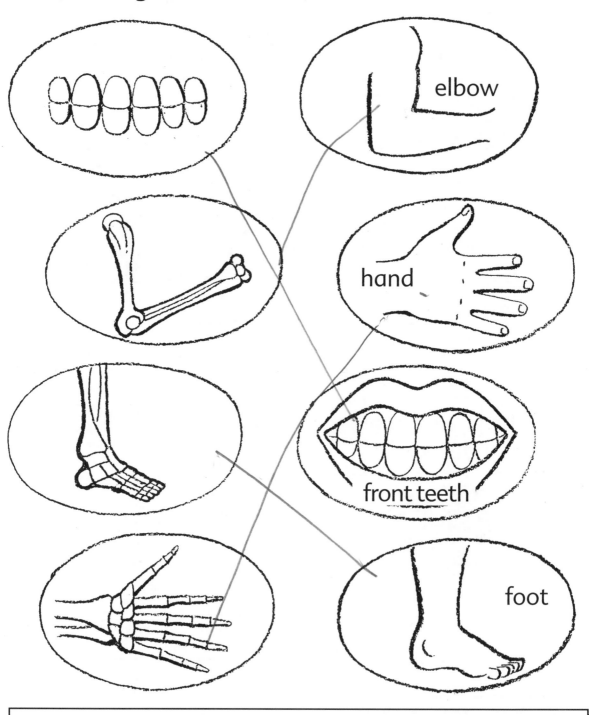

Join the correct parts of the body to their matching bones.

This is a **skeleton**.
It is made up of many bones.

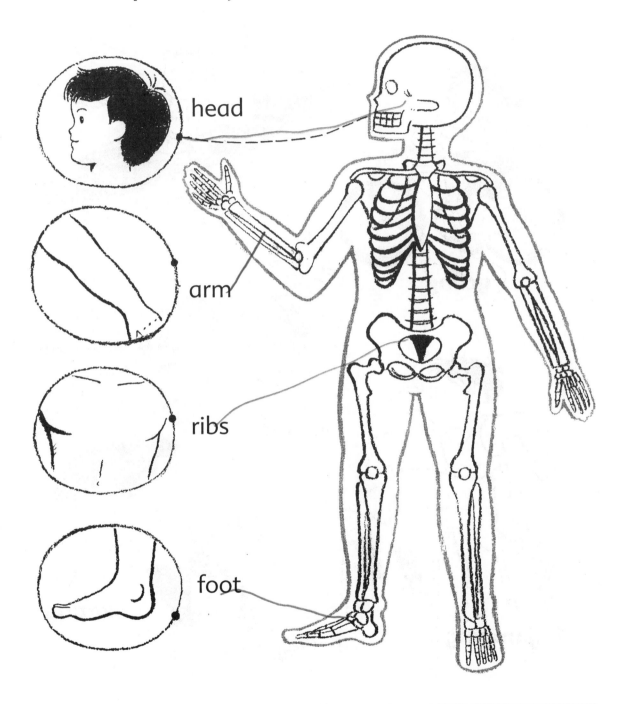

head

arm

ribs

foot

Draw lines to join the pictures to the matching bones on the skeleton.

Bones and muscles enable Shawn and Linda to do many things.

cycling

rowing

snorkelling

jumping

skating

- Colour the pictures.
- Trace the words and read them.

The **heart** pumps blood to all parts of the body.
The blood is carried in tubes called **blood vessels**.

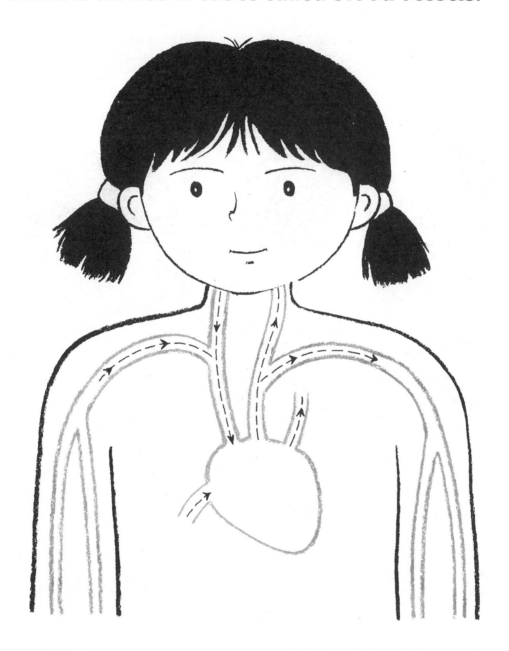

- Join the dotted lines with a red pencil to trace the blood flow.
- What colour do you think the heart should be? Colour it.

Your heart keeps pumping as long as you live.

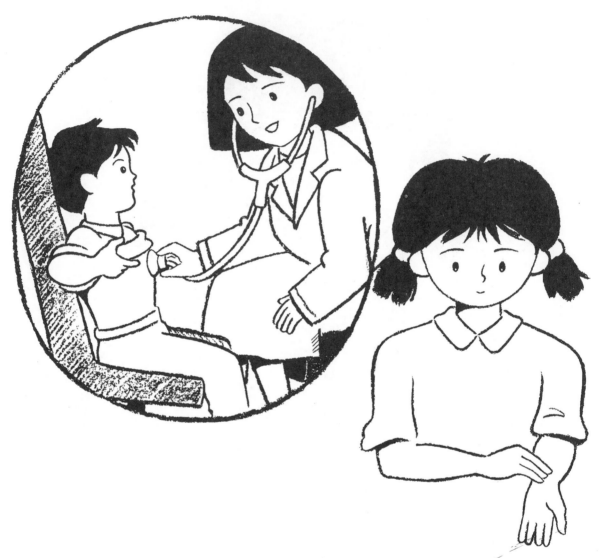

My heart beats _____ times in 1 minute.

- **Sit quietly and feel for your heartbeat.**
- **How many times does your heart beat in 1 minute?**

We breathe air into the lungs through the nose.

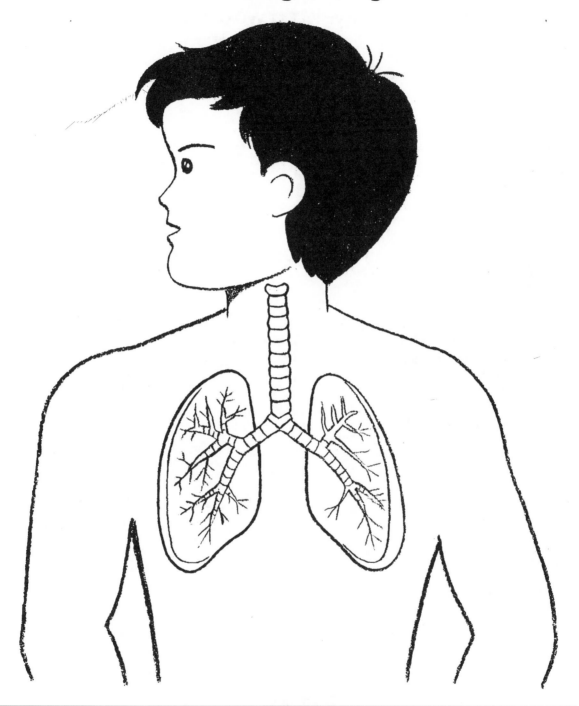

- Colour the lungs and windpipe.
- What will happen to a person if he stops breathing?

Shawn and Linda need to drink a lot of water.
They also pass out unwanted water as sweat and
urine.

- Colour the pictures.
- How much water do you drink a day?

Shawn and Linda need food to grow bigger.
The food goes into the mouth, then to the **stomach**.

fish and meat

vegetables

fruit

sweets

bread

chocolates

- **Which food should Shawn and Linda eat more of? Colour them.**
- **Which food should Shawn and Linda not eat too much of? Cross them out.**

The **stomach** and the **small intestine** break the food into smaller parts. What is not wanted is passed into the **big intestine**.

This is the small intestine.

This is the stomach

This is the big intestine.

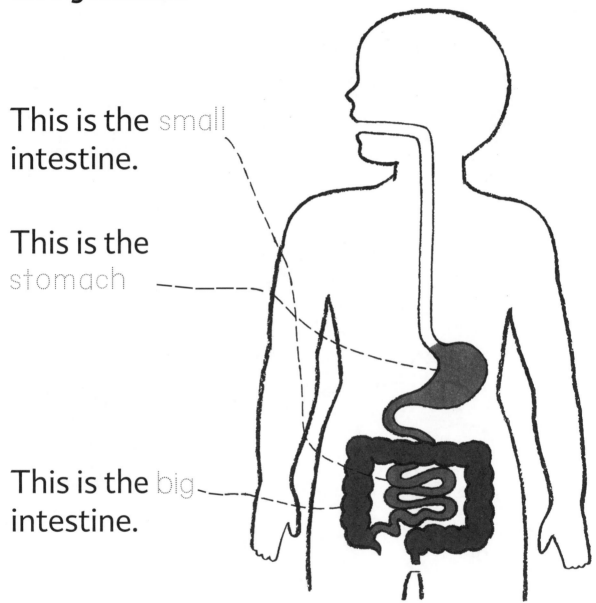

- Trace the words and read the sentences.
- Trace the dotted lines to join the sentences to the pictures.

Skin covers and protects our body.

Our skin looks like this!

- Colour Linda's skin yellow.
- Colour Shawn's skin brown.

What can Linda and Shawn feel?

cold

hot

painful

itchy

- Trace the words and read them.
- Colour the pictures.

Linda and Shawn also need many hours of sleep.

Draw what you think Linda and Shawn are
dreaming about. Then colour the pictures.

Shawn and Linda keep themselves clean.

Trace the dotted line to complete the drawings.

Our bodies are of different shapes and sizes.

(A) thin   (B) tall   (C) fat   (D) short

Write the letters A, B, C or D in the boxes to match the body shapes and sizes.

Children grow every day.

MALE	FEMALE

- How old are you?
- Colour the stage you are in now.

Animals

Some animals are big. Some are small.

frog

python

ant

cow

elephant

swallow

- Name the biggest animal on this page. Colour it.
- Name the smallest animal. Draw another one beside it.

Some animals live on land.

hen

crocodile

fox

squirrel

giraffe

- Draw any other animal that lives on land in the box.
- Say its name.

Some animals live in ponds, rivers and the sea.

goldfish

jellyfish

seahorse

octopus

shark

- Point to each animal and say its name.
- Draw any other animal that lives in water in the box. Say its name.

These animals live on land and in water.

seal

frog

crocodile

walrus

turtle

- Point to each animal and say its name.
- Colour the animals.

These animals are called mammals.
Their babies feed on milk.

cow

calf

cat

kitten

cub

bear

sheep

kangaroo

lamb

joey

- **Point to each baby on these two pages and say its name.**
- **Colour the baby animals.**

All baby birds are hatched from eggs.

hen

ducklings

duck

goslings

goose

chicks

Draw lines to join the mothers to their babies.

The babies of these animals are hatched from eggs, too.

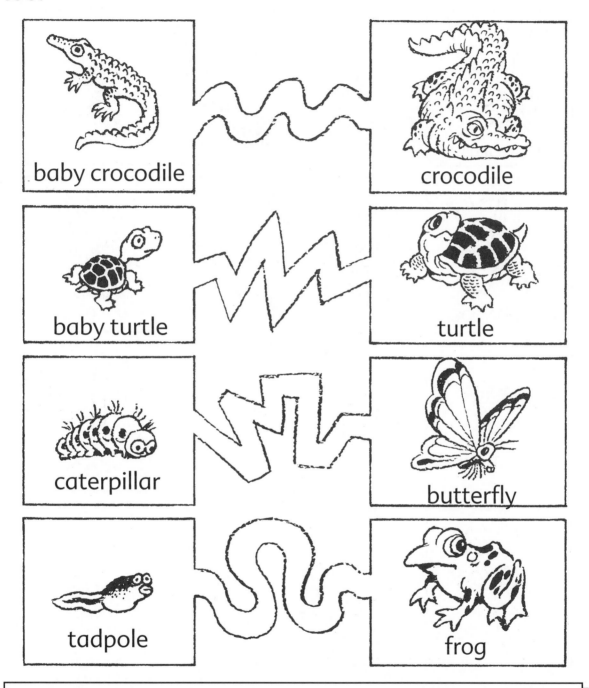

baby crocodile — crocodile

baby turtle — turtle

caterpillar — butterfly

tadpole — frog

- **Colour the paths that join the babies to their mothers.**
- **Say the names of these babies.**

Insects have six legs.

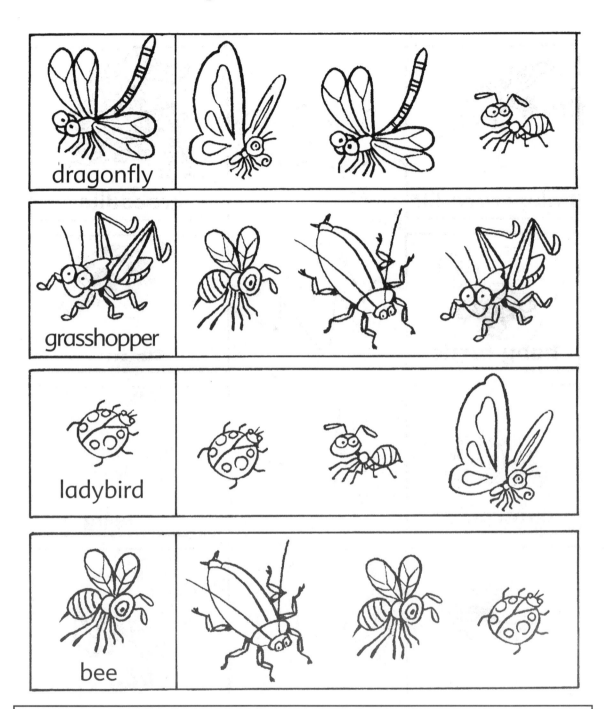

- How many legs has each insect?
- Which insect is the same as the first one? Circle it.
- Read the names of all the insects on this page.

The trunk is the nose of an elephant.
Do you know the parts of these animals' bodies?

mane

trunk

beak

fin

tail

wing

- Draw and colour the missing part of each animal.
- Name these parts.

Animals move around in different ways.
Some walk and run. Others crawl.

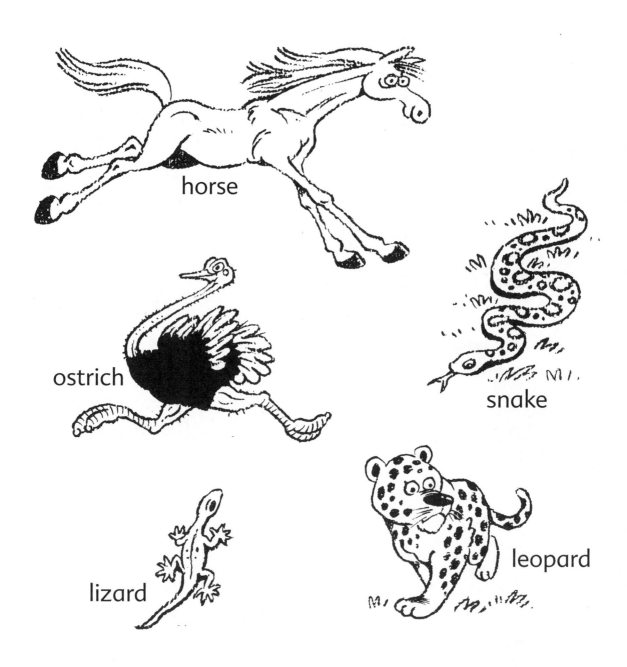

horse

snake

ostrich

lizard

leopard

- **Which animals walk or run? Colour them brown.**
- **Which animals crawl or slither? Colour them orange.**

Many animals that live in or near water can swim. Others, like the birds, can fly.

turtle

guppy

owl

bat

dolphin

housefly

- **Which of these animals fly? Circle them.**
- **Which of them swim? Colour them.**

Many animals eat plants only.

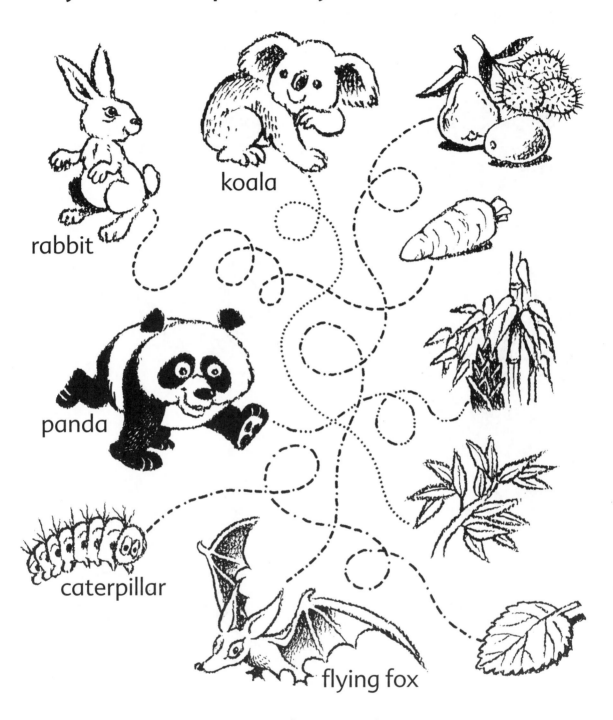

rabbit

koala

panda

caterpillar

flying fox

Trace the dotted lines and help these animals find their food.

These animals eat other animals.
Animals that are hunted and eaten are called prey.

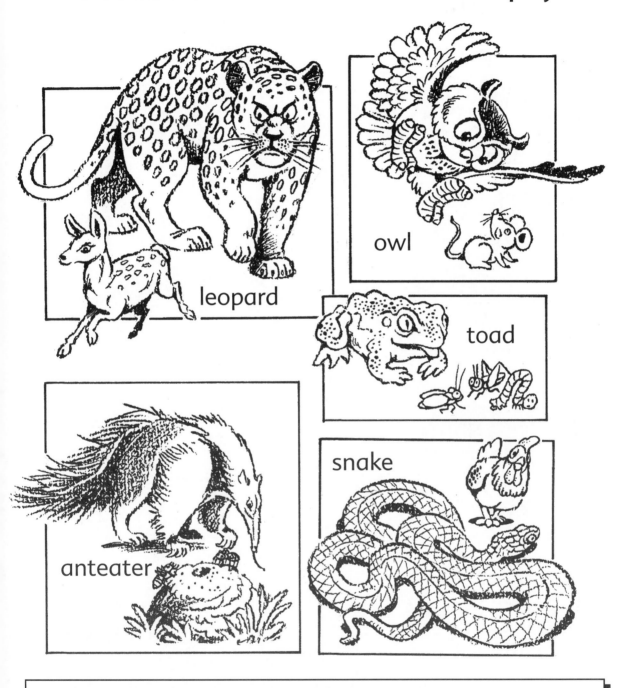

leopard

owl

toad

anteater

snake

- **What do these animals like to eat?**
- **Colour these meat-eating animals. Then circle their prey.**

39

These animals eat plants and other animals.

dog

hen

crow

mouse

- Join the animal to the food it eats.
- What is each animal eating?

These animals are dangerous.
Some can kill with their sharp teeth and claws.
Others can sting.

scorpion

shark

jellyfish

hornet

cheetah

- Draw in the missing parts.
- They are the dangerous parts of the animals.

These animals make their own homes.

nest

web

hive

burrow

- **Point to each home and say its name.**
- **Colour the picture.**

Many animals do not build their own homes.
They live in caves, woods or trees. Some live in
man-made homes.

woods

stable

den

trees

den

- Do you know where these animals live?
- Match the animals to their homes.

**Man has killed many of these animals.
They may not be found living on our earth in the
future.**

green turtle

tiger

blue whale

koala

Komodo dragon

panda

- **Do you know the names of all these endangered animals?**
- **Draw and colour these animals.**

Elephants are killed for their **tusks**.
Rhinoceroses are killed for their **horns**.

- Draw in the tusks and horns.

Gorillas and orangutans live in jungles. But they may not be found there in the future. Man is chopping down their homes.

- Colour these endangered animals.

Sadly, many animals are no longer living on Earth.
Here are two of them.

dodo

mammoth

- Say their names.
- Colour the animals.

Dinosaurs lived millions of years ago.

tyrannosaurus

brontosaurus

diplodocus

triceratops

stegosaurus

Colour these dinosaurs. Then try saying their names.

These animals can be kept as pets.

terrapin

goldfish

rabbit

hamster

bird

cat

dog

- Point to the animals and say their names.
- Colour three animals that you would like to keep as pets.

Plants

Some plants are big. Some are small.

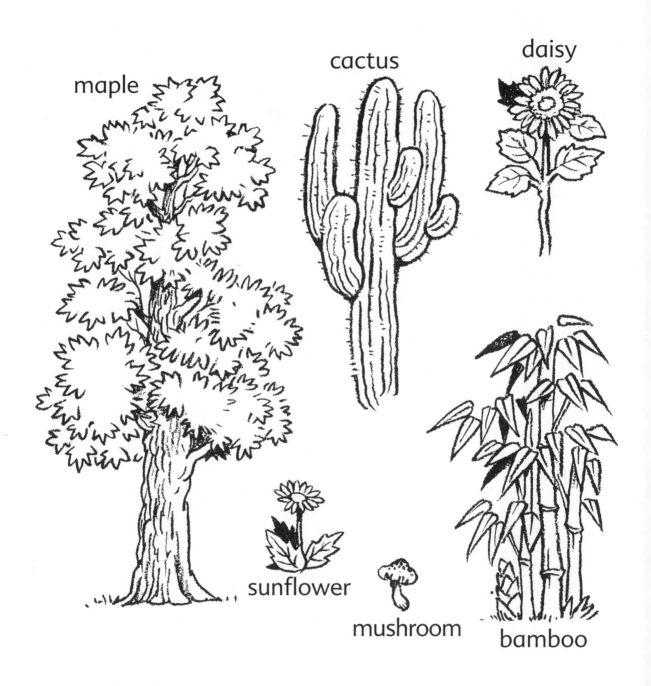

maple

cactus

daisy

sunflower

mushroom

bamboo

- **Colour the biggest plant on this page.**
- **Name the smallest plant and circle it.**

We call some big plants **trees**. They have **trunks**.

fir

pineapple

pine

morning glory

coconut

hazel

- **Cross out the two plants that are not trees.**
- **Colour the tree with the tallest trunk.**

This is a garden. There are many types of plants in a garden.

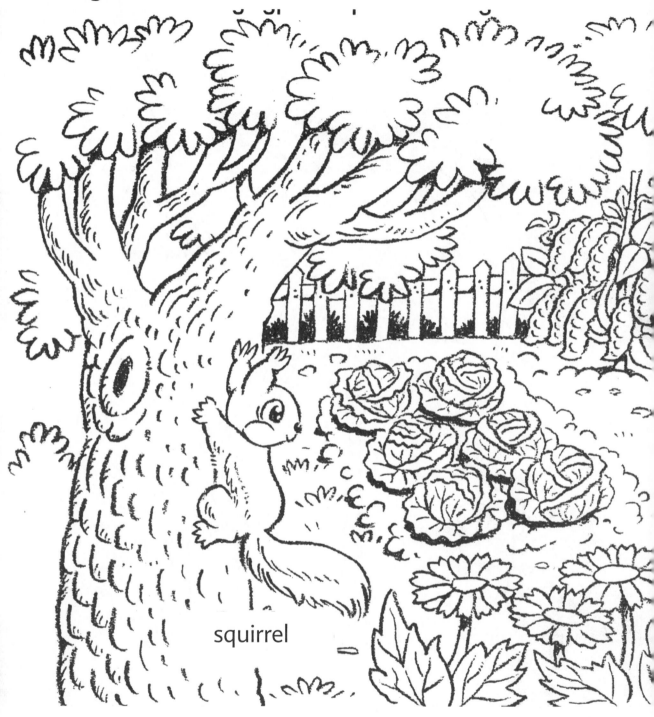

squirrel

butterfly

bee

- Circle the animals.
- Colour the whole picture.

A plant is made up of different parts.

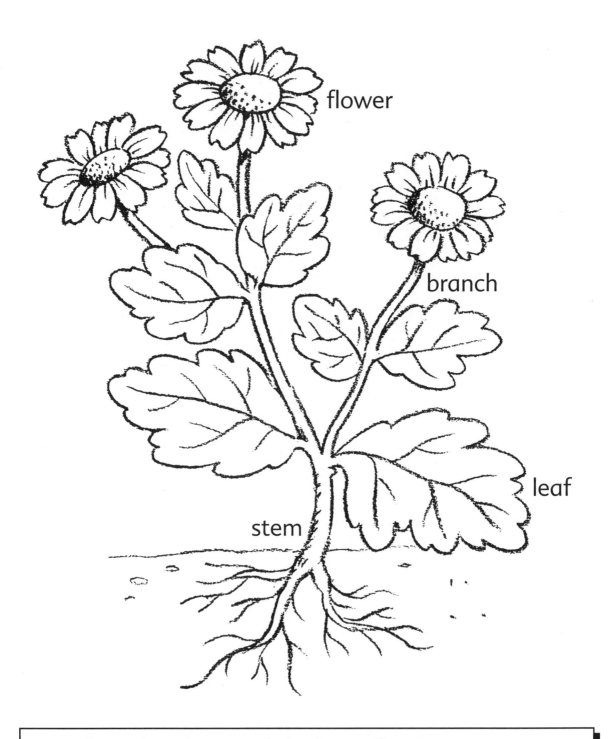

- Colour the stem and the branches brown.
- Colour the leaves green and the flowers red.

Roots are also part of a plant. Some plants have fat roots. Others have thin ones.

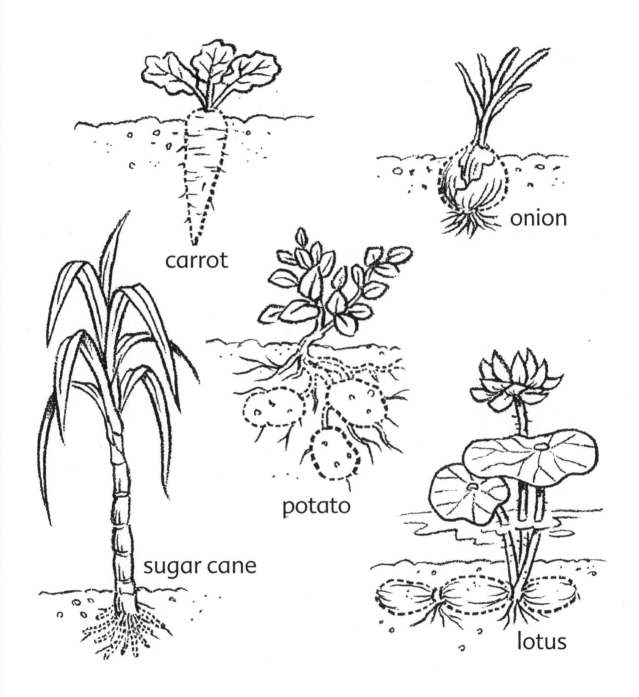

carrot

onion

potato

sugar cane

lotus

- Draw in the missing parts of the plants.
- Colour the roots you like to eat.

Some **leaves** are big. Others are small.
Some are broad. Others are long.

Match the leaves to the plants.

Some plants are grown for their leaves.

tea

pumpkin

lily

rice

cabbage

spinach

Which plants are grown for their leaves?
Colour them.

Flowers come in different colours and shapes.

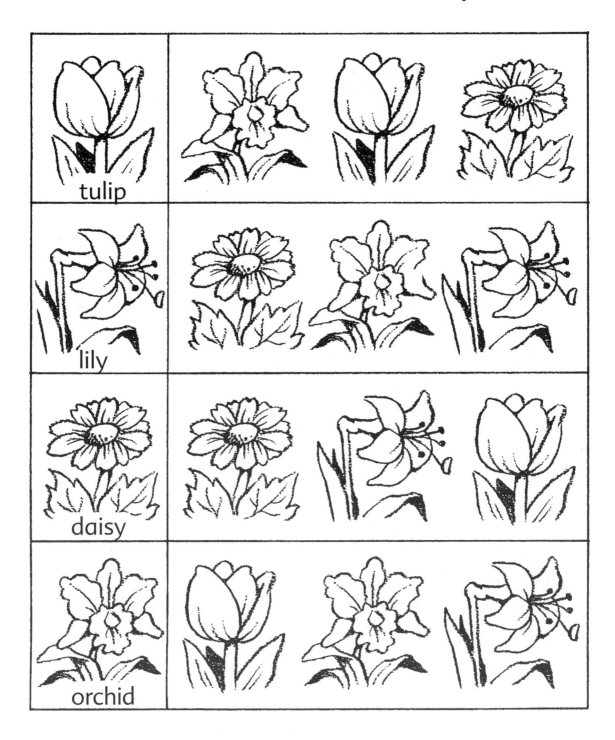

tulip

lily

daisy

orchid

Which flower is the same as the first one? Colour it.

Some flowers smell sweet.

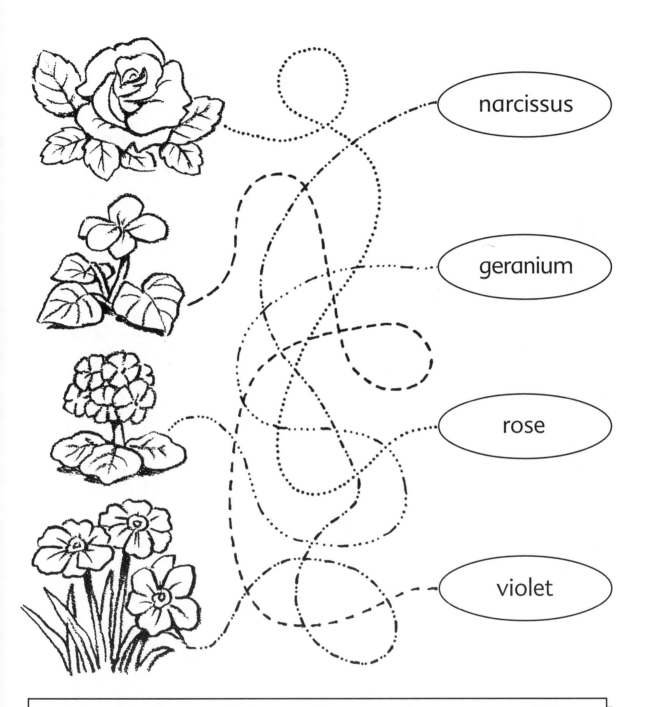

narcissus

geranium

rose

violet

- Join the dotted lines to find out the names of the flowers.
- Colour the flower you like best.

Fruits are formed after the flowers.

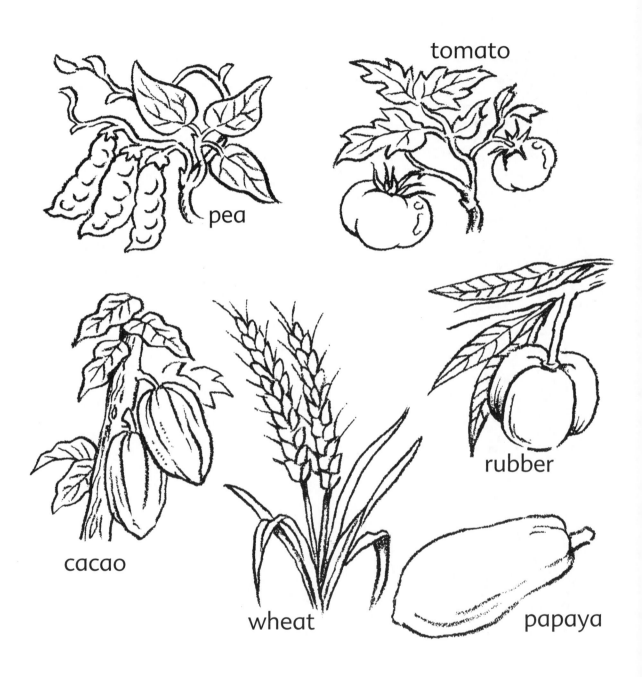

pea

tomato

cacao

wheat

rubber

papaya

- Can all these fruits be eaten?
- Colour only the edible fruits.

All these fruits are edible. Some are sweet. Some are rather sour and some are hot!

mango

banana

lemon

apple

coconut

chilli

- Colour the fruits.
- Draw a blue star next to the fruit you like to eat most.

There are seeds in the fruit.

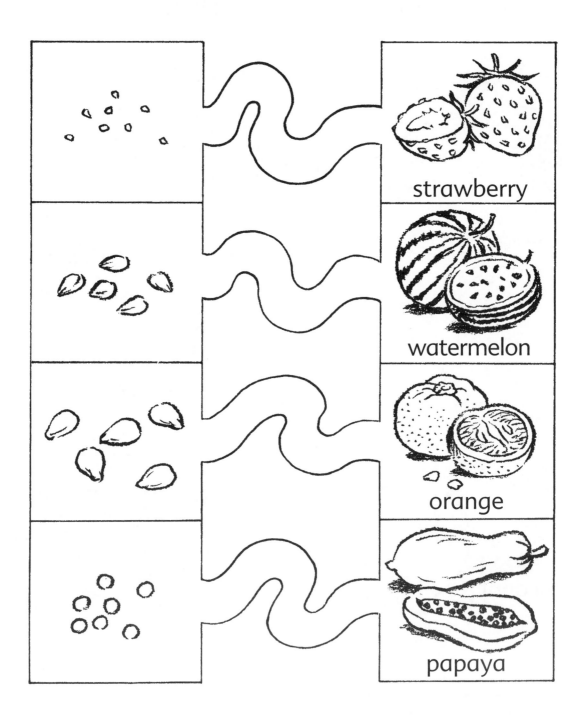

strawberry

watermelon

orange

papaya

- **Colour the path from the seeds to the fruits.**
- **Colour the seeds and flesh of the fruits.**

The seed grows into a new plant.
Plants need sunlight and water to grow.

After 3 days

After 6 days

After 9 days

After 12 days

Draw the sun, the clouds and the rain.

These plants are vegetables. They are grown as food.

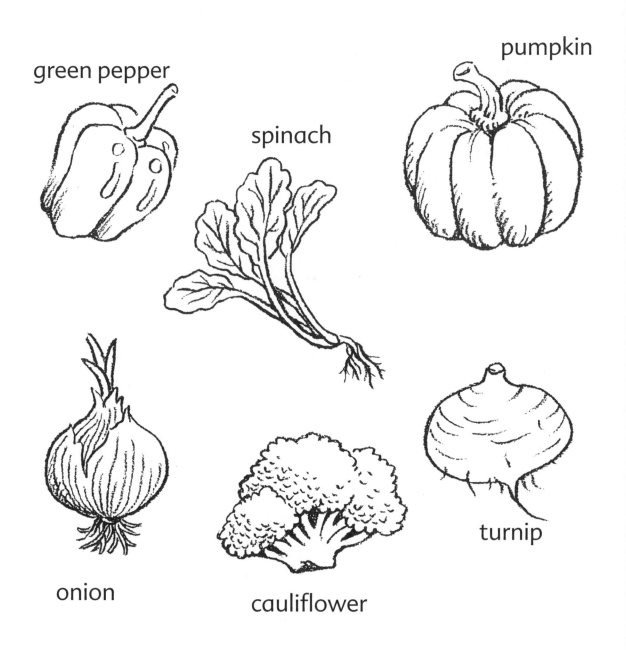

green pepper

spinach

pumpkin

onion

cauliflower

turnip

Colour the cauliflower and the pumpkin.

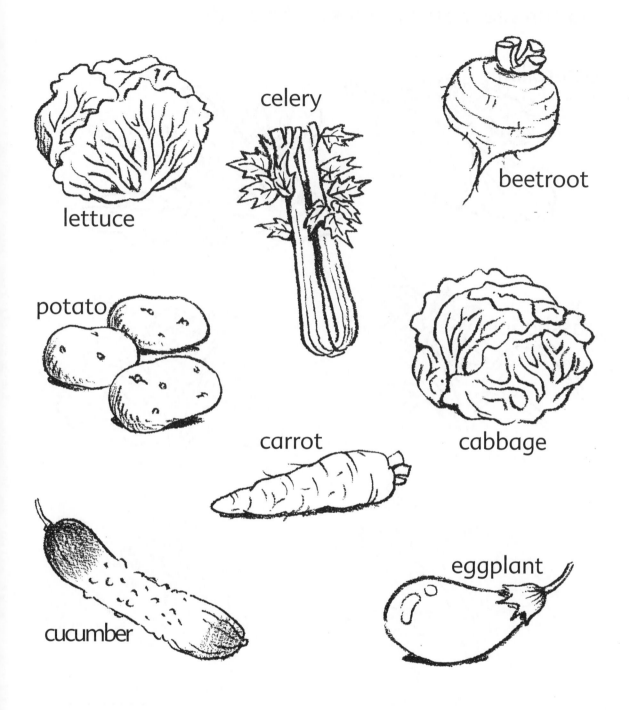

lettuce

celery

beetroot

potato

cabbage

carrot

cucumber

eggplant

- **How many of the vegetables can be used to make a salad? Colour three of them.**
- **Which vegetables do you like? Circle three of them.**

You can see these animals in the garden.

caterpillar

frog

grasshopper

snail

slug

ladybird

- **Name the animals which harm the plants.
Put a cross (X) next to them.**
- **Name the animals which help the plants.
Colour them.**

Some seeds are scattered by animals.

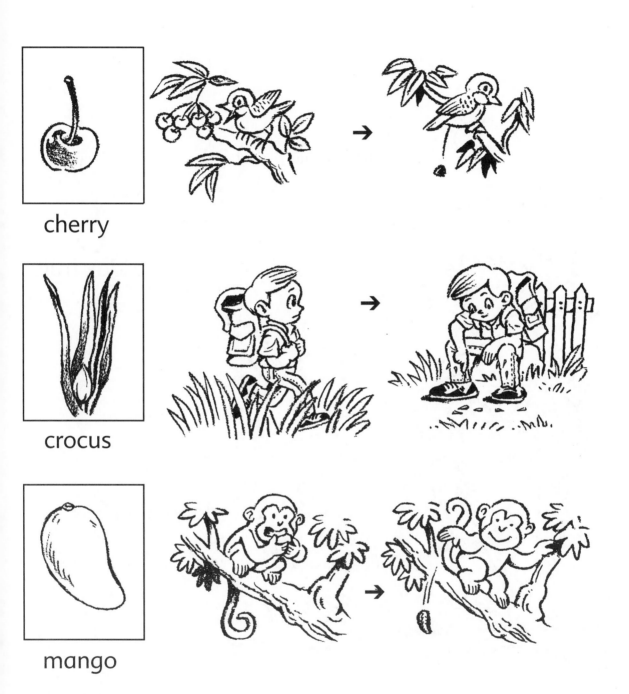

cherry

crocus

mango

- **Colour the fruits.**
- **Why does the monkey throw away the seed?**

These seeds are scattered by wind.

angsana

tridax fruit

maple

dandelion

Trace the fruits or seeds and colour them.
Why are they able to fly in the wind?

These fruits explode to scatter their seeds.

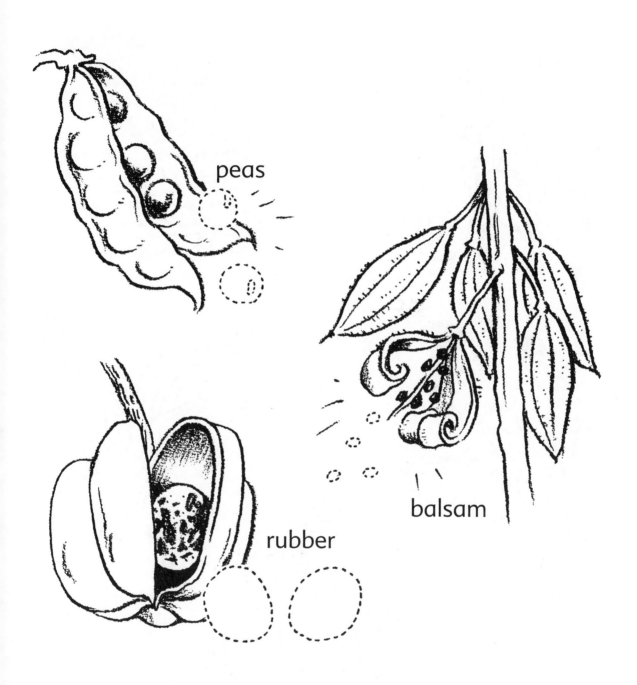

peas

balsam

rubber

Trace and colour the seeds. Are these seeds dry or wet?

We cannot eat some plants. They are **poisonous**.

poison ivy

aconite

poisonous
mushrooms

pong pong

dumb cane

Colour the plants.

These plants are unusual.

This is a desert plant. It has prickly spines, not leaves.

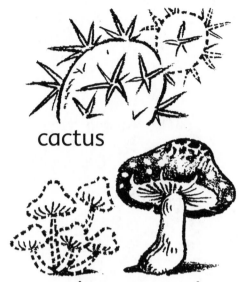

cactus

These plants have no leaves and flowers.

mushrooms and toadstools

This plant traps insects in its leaves and eats them.

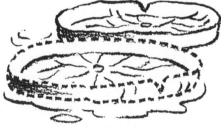

Venus's flytrap

This water plant has big leaves. Even a boy can sit on it.

Victoria regia

Draw and colour the missing parts.
They are the unusual parts of these plants.

We use **wood** to make many things.

- Colour the things made of wood.
- Draw a thing made of wood in the box.

Water

Rain is water that falls from the sky. The water goes into the ground, streams, rivers and seas.

Add more clouds and rain to the picture.

Colour the river and the sea.

Water can become steam or vapour.
It can become ice or snow, too.

steam

vapour

ice

snow

Trace the words.

Clouds in the sky are made up of small drops of water very close together.

Colour the cloud light grey.

When the clouds are full of water, they fall as rain.

Colour the cloud dark grey.

This is the **water cycle**.

Water vapour rises to form clouds.

rain

lake

river

sea

Sometimes after it rains, you can see a rainbow.

Colour the rainbow.

We give bodies of water different names.
They include sea, river, stream and pond.

(A) river   (B) pond   (C) sea   (D) stream

Write the letters A, B, C or D in the correct boxes.

The sea is salty. Many kinds of creatures live in it.

- Colour the creatures which live in the sea.
- Cross out the three creatures which do not live in the sea.

When a river comes to a cliff, it falls over. We call this a **waterfall.**

Colour the picture.

Plants need water to live.

- **Which picture comes first? And next?**
- **Write the numbers 1, 2, 3, 4 in the boxes.**

Animals also need water to live.

- Do you know that a camel stores a lot of water in its body so that it can travel for a long time without feeling thirsty?
- Colour a path to help the thirsty camel get to the water.

We also need to drink a lot of water to be healthy.

Draw the water containers by tracing the dotted lines.

Our food contains water.

milk

fruit

vegetables

fish and meat

- Colour the fruit in the bowl. Are they dry or juicy?
- Which is the juiciest vegetable in the picture?
- Which would you choose to get more water: milk, fish or meat?

These fruit contain a lot of water.

What colour is the juice in the glass? Colour it.
Then colour the other fruit.

Water helps to keep us cool.

- **Draw the things in the picture that we can use to keep ourselves cool.**
- **Colour the picture of the seaside.**

Water washes away dirt.

Draw in the missing parts of the picture.
They allow us to get water in the home.

Tap water comes from a **reservoir**.
The reservoir gets its water from rain.

Colour the reservoir.

Many plants live in water.

water lily

seaweed

pond

lotus

duckweed

sea

These are water plants.
Which one is found in the sea?

Besides fish, many other creatures live in a pond.
Here are some of them.

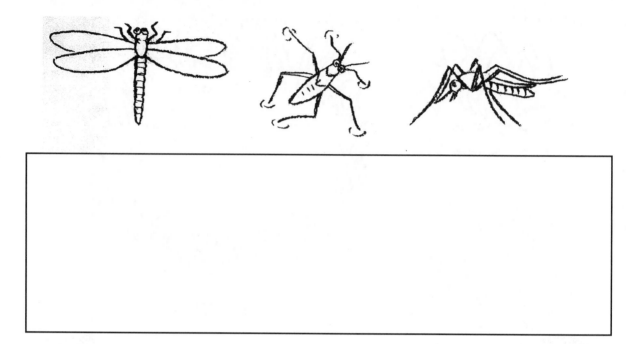

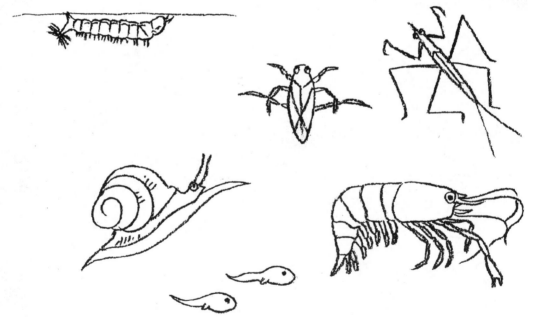

- Colour the creatures.
- Draw in the box another creature which is not found in this picture.

There are birds that swim or walk in water to look for food.

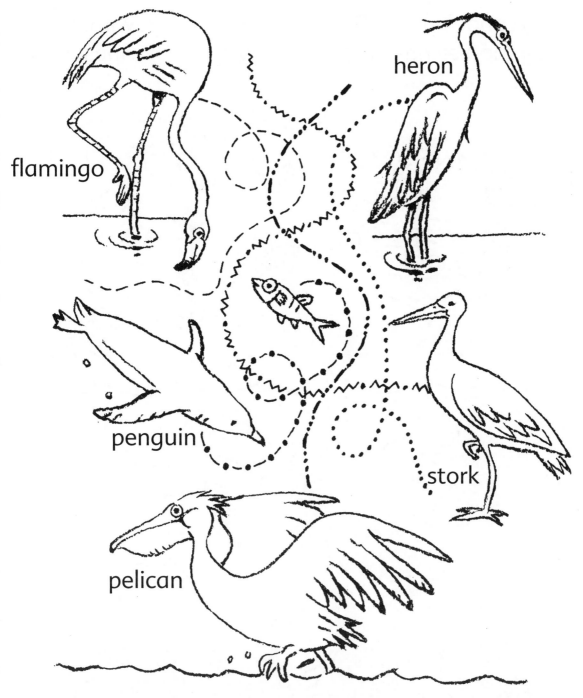

flamingo

heron

penguin

stork

pelican

- Trace the dotted lines to see which bird has the fish.
- Then colour the bird and the fish.

We can have great fun with water.

(A) canoeing   (B) water-skiing   (C) swimming
(D) snorkelling   (E) scuba-diving   (F) windsurfing

- Colour the things that help the people enjoy the water.
- Write the correct letter in the boxes.

Water is precious. We should not waste it.

Who is wasting water? Draw a cross in the boxes for the persons wasting water.

Air

There is air around us.
We cannot see air, but can feel it when it is moving.

Which picture shows that air is moving?
Colour that picture.

Moving air is called **wind**.

Complete the drawings. Then colour the pictures.

A very strong wind is called a **hurricane** or **typhoon**.

Colour the pictures.

We need air to live. Divers need air to stay underwater.
They carry an oxygen tank on their back.

Colour the equipment for diving.
What is in the tank?

An **astronaut** has to wear a spacesuit containing air when he is outside his space shuttle.

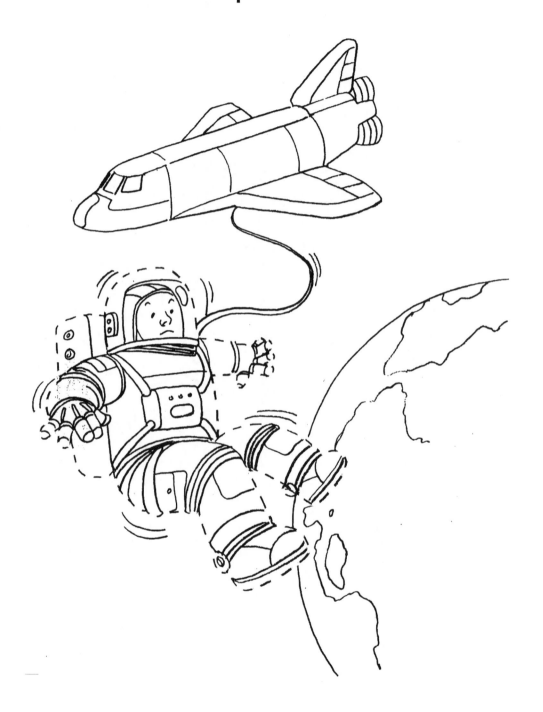

Join the dots and draw the astronaut.

A plant needs air to live. It also needs air to make food.

air

Write the word in the box.
What will happen to a plant that is kept in space?

Plants want their seeds to travel so that they can grow in places far away.

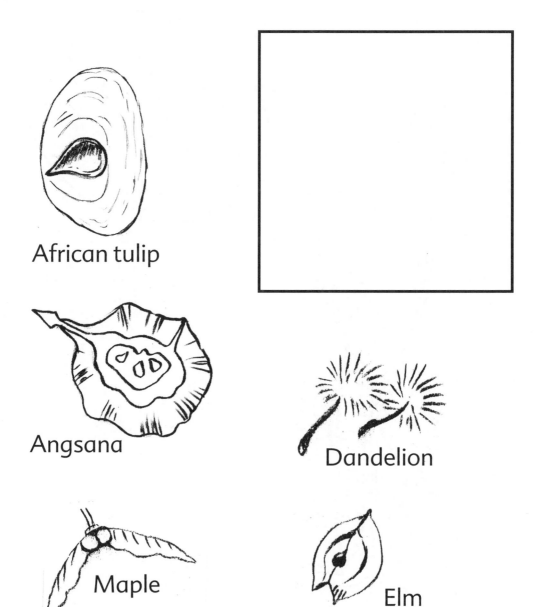

African tulip

Angsana

Dandelion

Maple

Elm

- **What helps these fruit and seeds travel?**
- **Are they light or heavy?**
- **Draw a fruit or seed that the wind can blow away.**

There is air in water. Fish need air.
They take in air in the water with their **gills**.

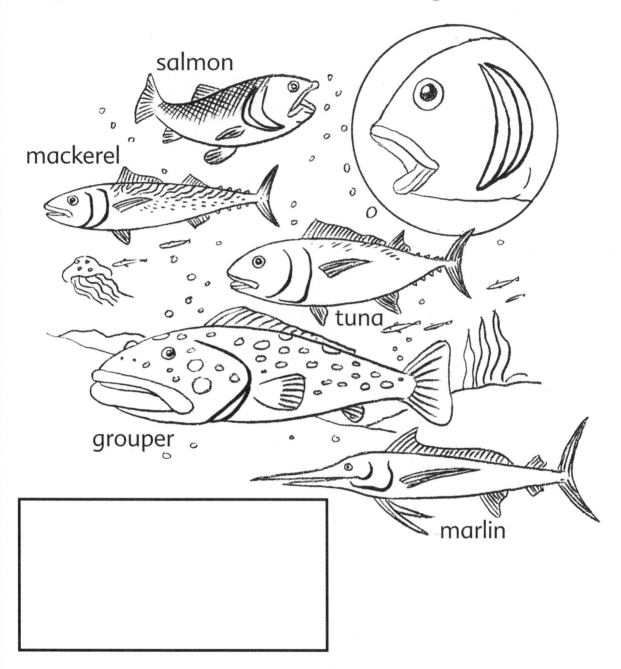

- salmon
- mackerel
- tuna
- grouper
- marlin

- Read the names of the different fishes.
- Circle the gills with a colour pencil.
- Draw your favourite fish in the box.

There is air in soil.

Try this!

1. Put some garden soil into a glass.

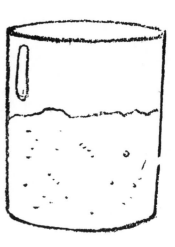

2. Fill the glass with water.

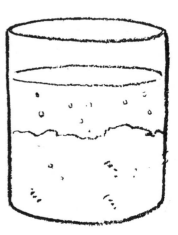

3. What comes out of the soil?

   Answer: Tiny bubbles of ⬚ .

Complete the answer in 3.

Air contains water.

Try this!

1. Pour ice-cold water into a glass.

2. Look at the outer side of the glass
   What do you see?

   Answer: There is [   ]
   on the outer side of the glass.

**Complete the answer.
Where does the water come from?**

The air in this place is **fresh**.
The trees are green and healthy. The birds are happy.

- Colour the picture.
- How many birds are there?
- You may want to draw other animals such as squirrels, bees and butterflies.

The air in this place is cold.

thermometer

- Colour the picture.
- How cold do you think it is? What will the thermometer show? What will the thermometer show in your room?

The air in this place is smelly.

Colour the things which make this place smelly and dirty.

In some places, vehicles and buildings give off poisonous gases. They **pollute** the air.

- Which of these things pollute the air?
- Put a cross (X) beside the things which pollute the air.
- Put a pass (✔) for the rest of the pictures.

The air is also polluted when things burn.

Colour the place where the air is fresh.

We need fresh air to live healthily.

- Colour the path to help the two children go where the air is fresh.
- Colour also the place they want to go.

In cold weather, we can warm up the cold air in the room.

fireplace

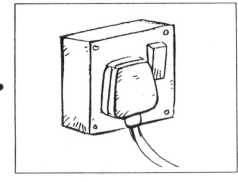

electricity

radiator

wood

- What is used to make heat in the fireplace and radiator?
- Use lines to match the pictures.

In hot weather, we can cool ourselves.

We use a hand fan.

We use an electric fan.

We use an air-conditioner.

Colour the things we can use to keep cool.

There are other things that make use of air to do work.

a hot-air balloon

a hair-dryer

a vacuum cleaner

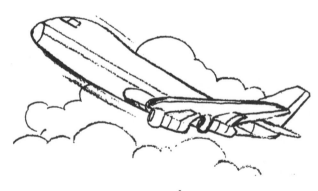

an aeroplane

Colour the objects.

With the wind, we are able to do these things.

to fly kites

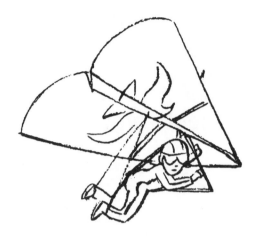

to hang-glide

to windsurf

to show the direction of the wind

- Colour the pictures.
- What will happen if the wind suddenly stops?

We must blow air into some **instruments** to produce sound.

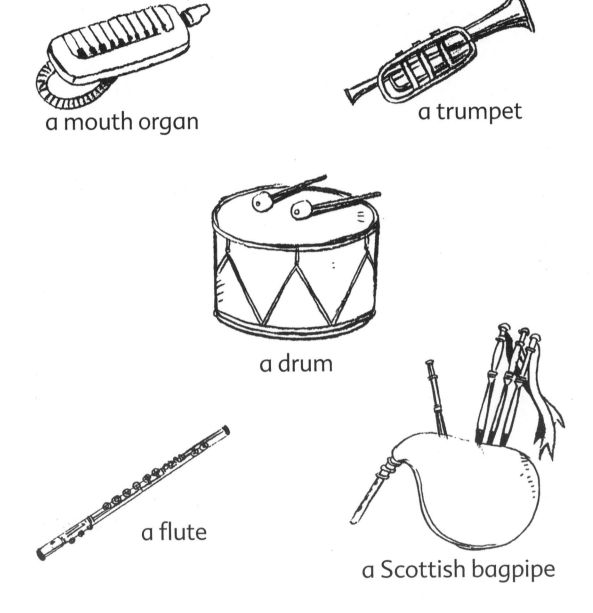

a mouth organ

a trumpet

a drum

a flute

a Scottish bagpipe

- Cross out the instrument that is not a wind instrument.
- Colour the wind instrument you are learning to play or would like to play.

The things on the left need air to make them work.

- Draw lines to pair up the pictures.
- What is a flat tyre?

These creatures use air in a strange way.

- Colour the pictures.
- Why do the puffer and the toad want to make themselves look big?

The Earth

We live on the Earth. It is round and beautiful, isn't it?

Colour all the seas blue.

Where is the sun in the evening?
The sun is in the west**.**

- **Complete the sentence.**
- **Colour the sun in the picture.**

Which is moving, the merry-go-round or the tree?
Answer: The merry-go-round / tree.

Which is moving, the Sun or the Earth?
Answer: The Sun / Earth.

Circle the right answer.

The air surrounds the Earth.
It is called the **wind** when it is moving.

Colour the picture.

The side of the Earth facing the sun has daylight. The side of the Earth facing **away** from the sun has night.

Colour the side of the earth which is having night.

Draw one thing you do during the day and one thing you do at night.

This mountain has a big opening at the top. From time to time, melted rocks and gases come out of it. We call this mountain a **volcano**.

Colour the melted rocks.

A large area of water is called the **sea**. We use boats and ships to move on the sea.

Colour the path to help the ship reach land.

Our Earth is very big. Some places on Earth are very cold.

fox

polar bear

Eskimo

reindeer

Six foxes are hidden in this picture.
Can you find and colour them?

Some places are very hot and dry.

• **Colour the hot sun and the cactus.**

Some places are not too hot nor too cold. They are suitable for plants to grow and animals and people to live in.

- Colour the picture.
- What will water turn into when it is very cold?
- What will it turn into when it is very hot?

We rear some animals on land.

goat

duck

turkey

- **Trace the words and read them.**
- **Colour the picture.**

We use land to grow vegetables, fruit and cereals.

corn

banana

cabbage

sugar cane

- Trace the words and read them.
- Colour the picture.

Many people work and live here. There are many buildings. We call this place a **town**.

Colour the picture.

Animals also live on Earth. Some live in water, others live on land.

ant

cuttlefish

swan

coral

whale

Join the animals to where they live.

Would you like to live in a place like this?

Put a cross (X) next to the actions we should not do.

We love our planet Earth.
We must keep it clean, green and peaceful.

Put a tick (✔) next to the actions the children are doing to keep the place clean and green.

How can we help to keep the beach clean?

Redraw a clean beach in the second box.